HOOKED ON
MEASUREMENT

**User-friendly activities
that develop students' skills in measurement**

AGES 9–13

Jo Issa

Title:	Hooked on Measurement
Author:	Jo Issa
Editor:	Tanya Tremewan
Designer:	Diane Whitford
Book code:	PB00073
ISBN:	978-1-908735-53-9
Published:	2012
Publisher:	TTS Group Ltd
	Park Lane Business Park Kirkby-in-Ashfield Notts, NG17 9GU Tel: 0800 318 686 Fax: 0800 137 525
Websites:	www.tts-shopping.com
Copyright:	Text: © Jo Issa, 2011
	Edition and illustrations: © TTS Group Ltd, 2012
About the author:	Jo Issa is an experienced teacher who has taught in both the UK and New Zealand. She is passionate about making maths fun and providing students with the tools they need to solve maths problems independently.

Contents

Introduction

Hooked on Measurement is designed to complement your classroom numeracy programme with user-friendly activities that develop students' practical skills using length, area, volume, capacity, weight, time, speed and angles. Each section includes real-world problems that encourage students to apply mental strategies, along with task cards that encourage exploration and discussion. Through measurement activities, students will apply knowledge and strategies gained through numeracy teaching.

Hooked on Measurement is part of a series that supports the teaching of measurement, geometry and statistics. This series is aimed at students in Years 6 to 8; depending on the ability level of your class, you may also find it useful for extending Year 5 students and supporting Year 9 students.

How to use this book

Each section, covering an area of measurement, includes basic activities for practice, problem-solving questions and task cards that extend students' thinking within mathematical contexts. For easy reference, each activity page is headed with the learning intention.

The practice activities are designed to be completed independently while the problems, games and task cards are ideal for pairs or small groups. Explanations are provided where relevant on activity pages and answers are included at the back of the book.

Collecting resources

Many resources will be available in the classroom. Students will also need:

- rulers
- tape measures
- analogue clock faces
- stopwatches
- thermometers
- kitchen scales
- bathroom scales
- protractors.

Curriculum links

Shape, space and measures

Strand	Sub strand	Objectives
Measures and construction	Measures	• Interpret scales on a range of measuring instruments, including those for time and mass; know that measurements using real numbers depend on the choice of unit; recognise that measurements given to the nearest whole unit may be inaccurate by up to one half in either direction; convert measurements from one unit to another; make sensible estimates of a range of measures in everyday settings. • Understand angle measure, using the associated language.
	Construction	• Measure and draw lines to the nearest millimetre, and angles to the nearest degree; draw triangles and other 2-D shapes using a ruler and protractor, construct cubes, regular tetrahedra, square-based pyramids and other 3-D shapes from given information.
	Mensuration	• Find areas of rectangles, recalling the formula, understanding the connection to counting squares and how it extends this approach; recall and use the formulae for the area of a parallelogram and a triangle; find the surface area of simple shapes using the area formulae for triangles and rectangles; calculate perimeters and areas of shapes made from triangles and rectangles. • Find volumes of cuboids, recalling the formula and understanding the connection to counting cubes.
	Loci	• Find loci, both by reasoning and by using ICT to produce shapes and paths.

Source: Adapted from *The National Curriculum for England*, 1999, Programme of study for Mathematics at Key Stage 3, curriculum.qcda.gov.uk

Use scales to estimate and measure lengths

A. Use the scale to estimate the length of each of these objects.

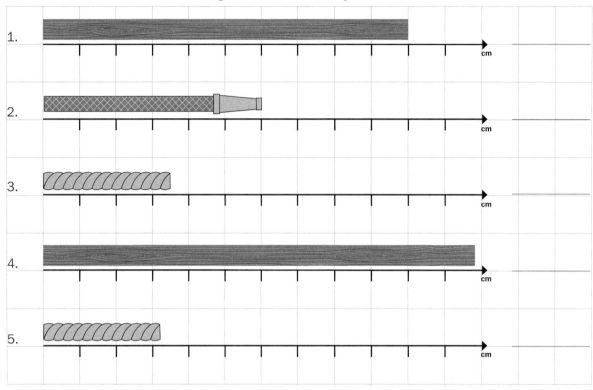

B. Record the length of each object using the scale.

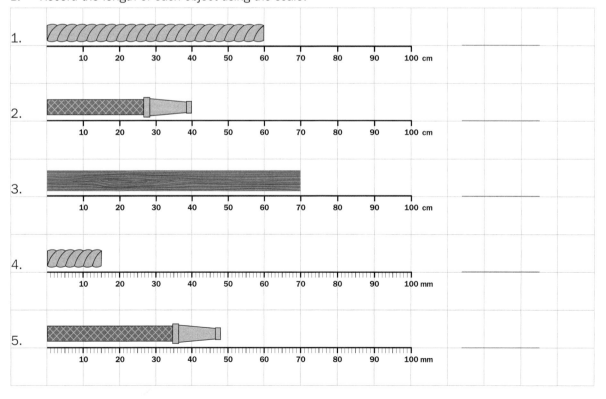

Length

Estimate lengths

Use the 1 cm line as a guide to estimate the length of the thick line on each shape below.

▬ 1 cm

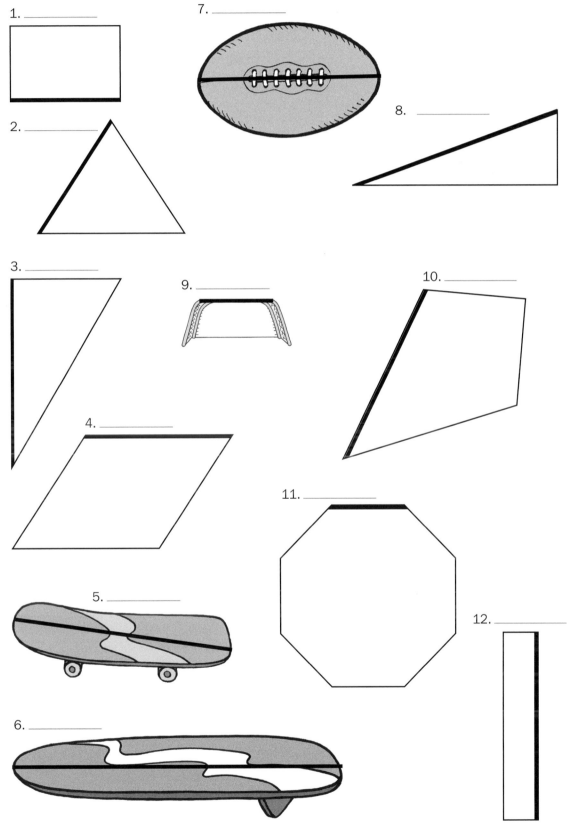

1. _____

2. _____

3. _____

4. _____

5. _____

6. _____

7. _____

8. _____

9. _____

10. _____

11. _____

12. _____

7

Measure lengths

Find the length of each line using centimetres. Then convert the unit measurement from centimetres to millimetres and write your answer above the line.

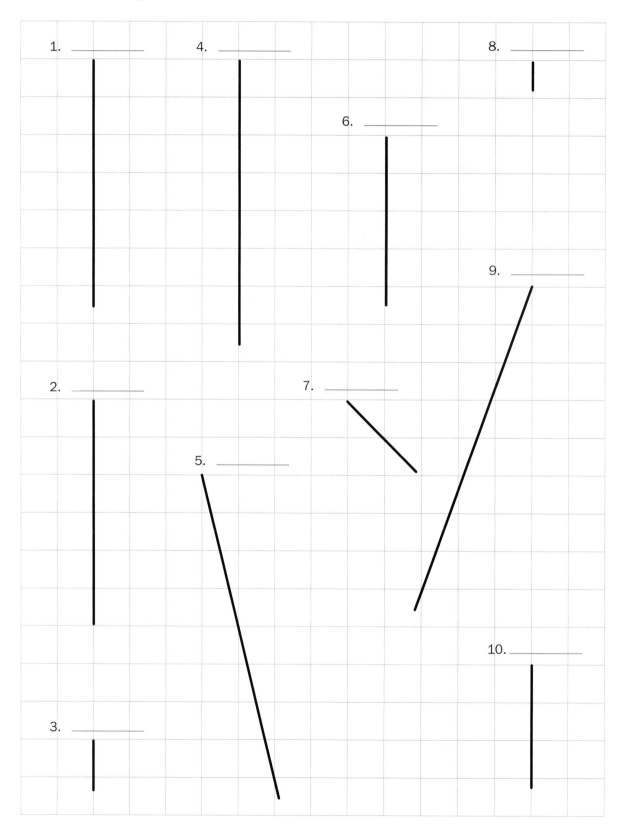

1. _____

2. _____

3. _____

4. _____

5. _____

6. _____

7. _____

8. _____

9. _____

10. _____

Length

Measure lengths and convert unit measurements

A. Find the length of the thick line on each shape and record your answer in centimetres.

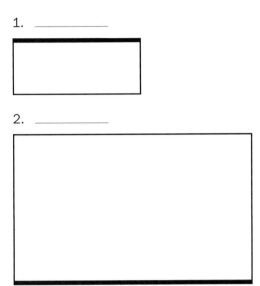
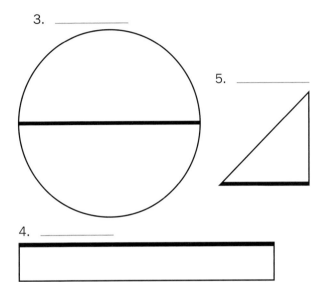

1. _____
2. _____
3. _____
4. _____
5. _____

B. Find the length of the thick line on each shape and record your answer in millimetres.

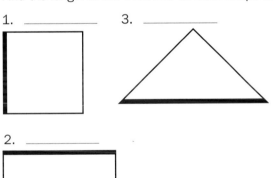

1. _____
2. _____
3. _____
4. _____
5. _____

C. Draw a line to connect measurements that are equal.

34 cm	1.2 cm	109 cm	1.5 cm
15 mm	99 mm	27 mm	
2.7 cm	340 mm	12 mm	89 mm
8.9 cm	9.9 cm	1 090 mm	

© TTS Group Ltd, 2012   **9**

Convert between kilometres and metres using whole numbers and decimals

A. Below are the distances Jon runs during one week of fitness training. Complete the table by converting between kilometres and metres as needed.

	Distance	
	in km	in m
1.	1.5	
2.	1.75	
3.		220
4.	2.75	
5.	2.8	
6.		195
7.		1 236
8.		5 879

B. Jon's friends sign up for a six-week fitness programme. Find the total distance (in metres) covered by each person and convert each total to kilometres.

Exercise	Jan (m)	Henry (m)	Miriama (m)	Kes (m)	Jenny (m)
Log rolling	230	310	257	289	299
Step challenge	150	150	150	150	150
Ladder sprint	125	150	175	125	150
Time trial	1 200	1 250	1 360	1 400	1 100
Total in m					
Total in km					

C. Jerry has recorded the distances he biked on an eight-day tour in metres. Convert each distance to kilometres.

1. 101 106 m _____
2. 97 204 m _____
3. 126 125 m _____
4. 74 102 m _____

5. 9 879 m _____
6. 105 586 m _____
7. 54 125 m _____
8. 77 012 m _____

D. Hayley is preparing her swimming training programme for the month. Help her convert each distance to metres.

1. Back stroke 2.4 km = _____ m
2. Freestyle 5.8 km = _____ m

3. Butterfly 1.7 km = _____ m
4. Breast stroke 4.5 km = _____ m

Find the perimeter of shapes

Find the perimeter of each shape by measuring the distance around it.

For example: The perimeter of this rectangle is 2 cm + 3 cm + 2 cm + 3 cm = 10 cm

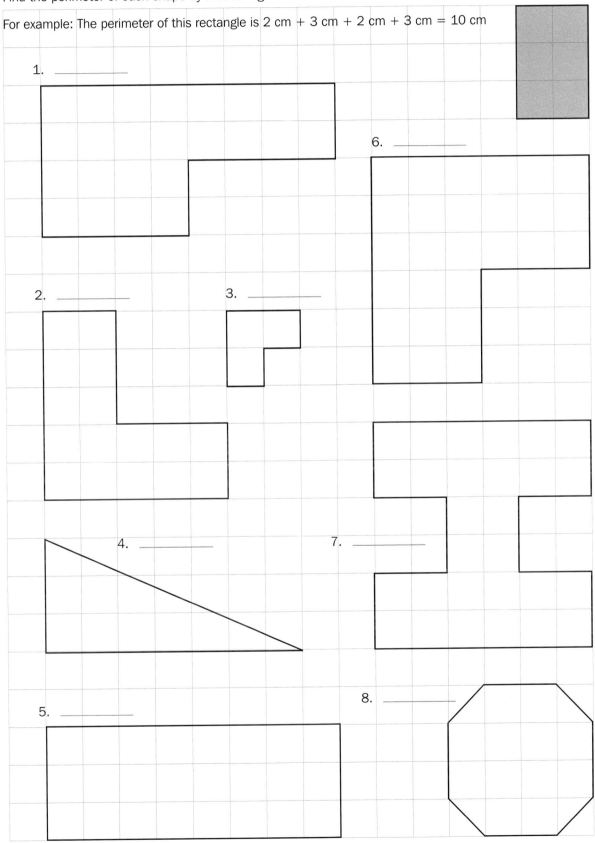

1. _____

2. _____

3. _____

4. _____

5. _____

6. _____

7. _____

8. _____

Find the perimeter of complex shapes

A. Find the perimeter of each shape.

1. _____

2. _____

3. _____

4. _____

B. Calculate the length of the missing side(s)
and then find the perimeter of each shape.

1. x = _____   Perimeter = _____

2. x = _____   y = _____   Perimeter = _____

3. x = _____
   y = _____
   Perimeter = _____

Shape B1:
5 cm (top), 5 cm (left), 3 cm, x, 2 cm, 2 cm

Shape B2:
6 cm, 1 cm, x, 5 cm, y, 3 cm

Shape B3:
y, 1 cm, x, 2.5 cm, 6 cm, 2 cm

C. Find the missing length of each shape.

1. x = _____

14 m, 5 m, 10 m, 25 m, x

2. Perimeter = 32 m
   Length of a = _____

4 m, a

Solve problems involving length

A. Help Jez select the most appropriate unit of measurement to suit each task.

1. The width of a soccer goal _____

2. The height of a rugby post _____

3. The width of his laptop _____

4. The width of a shoelace _____

5. The length of a running track _____

B. The table below shows how many lengths each member of a swimming squad has swum in a 25-metre pool. Complete the table to show how far each member has swum in metres.

Lengths swum	Distance swum (m)
1. 8 × 25 metres	
2. 25 × 25 metres	
3. 19 × 25 metres	
4. 27 × 25 metres	
5. 40 × 25 metres	

C. Four golf players have to cover 201 m from tee off to reach the next hole. Each of them has taken one shot and covered the distance shown below. Find the distance each golf player still needs to shoot to reach the next hole.

Golfer	Distance covered after 1 shot	Distance to hole (m)
1. Justin	117 m	
2. Rory	115 m	
3. Colin	125 m	
4. Fred	142 m	

D. Find the total number of lengths of wood required to line each of the following pathways. Wood is sold in lengths of 0.25 metres.

Path number	Required distance for path	Number of lengths of wood needed
1	65 m	
2	37 m	
3	95 m	

E. A metalworker designs a sculpture for an exhibition. Three of her designs are shown below. Find an accurate method to measure each design then answer the questions that follow.

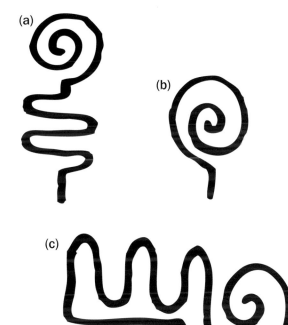

(a)

(b)

(c)

1. Which design uses the least metal? _____

2. Which design uses the most metal? _____

Task card 1   Measure up   Length

Find two objects that are the same length as each of the measurements below.

3 metres   **5 centimetres**   **0.5 centimetres**

_____   _____   _____

_____   _____   _____

1.5 metres   **10 metres**

_____   _____

_____   _____

Task card 2   Designer Jewels   Length

You have 30 cm of metal-coated wire to incorporate in a piece of jewellery. When you've decided on a design, draw it below. Remember to show the correct dimensions on your design.

Find the area of shapes including irregular shapes

The units we use to measure area are **centimetres squared** (cm²), **metres squared** (m²) and **kilometres squared** (km²).

When we calculate area, we multiply the length by the width. For example, the rectangle on the right is 3 cm by 7 cm so the area is 21 cm².

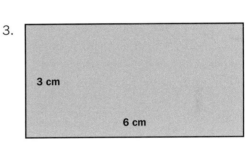

3 cm

7 cm

A. Calculate each of the following areas.

1.

5 cm

7 cm

Area = _____

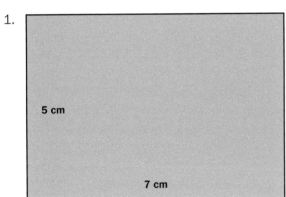

3.

3 cm

6 cm

Area = _____

2.

3 cm

4 cm

Area = _____

4.

3.5 cm

7 cm

Area = _____

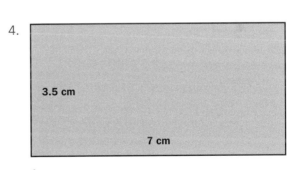

B. Joss is putting together quotes for customers who want a ready lawn. To do this, she needs to work out the area of each customer's lawn plot. Find the area of each of these plots.

1. 30 m × 4 m   Area = _____

2. 45 m × 19 m Area = _____

3. 60 m × 24 m Area = _____

4. 90 m × 67 m Area = _____

5. 55 m × 78 m Area = _____

6. 25 m × 13 m Area = _____

7. 72 m × 40 m Area = _____

8. 15 m × 12 m Area = _____

9. 38 m × 20 m Area = _____

10. 42 m × 16 m Area = _____

Find the area of triangles

To find the area of a triangle, make it into a square or rectangle then find the area of the shape and halve it.

For example: Half of 16 cm² = 8 cm²

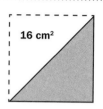

16 cm²

Find the area of each of these triangles.

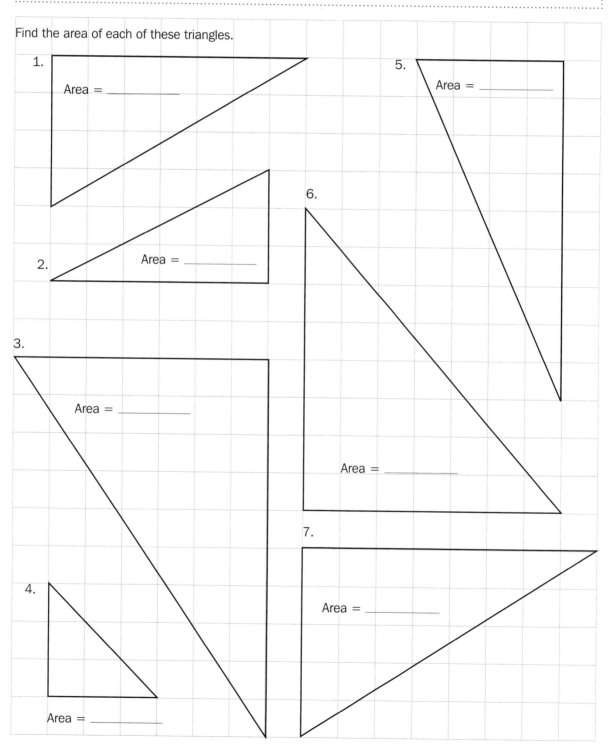

1. Area = _____

2. Area = _____

3. Area = _____

4. Area = _____

5. Area = _____

6. Area = _____

7. Area = _____

Find the area of complex shapes

To find the area of a complex shape, look for an easy shape to work with.

For example, to work out the area of shape (a), extend the shape into a rectangle then subtract shape (b) from the area of the rectangle.

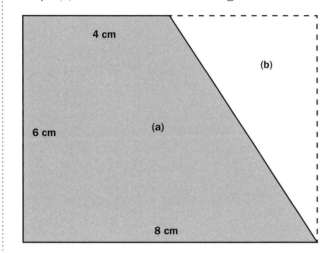

8 cm × 6 cm = 48 cm²

Calculate the area of (b) which is 12 cm². (Tip: To find the area of the triangle, we make the triangle into a rectangle then halve it.)

Then to find the area of (a), subtract the area of (b) from the area of the whole rectangle:

48 cm² − 12 cm² = 36 cm²

Use the strategy above to work out the area of each of the following shapes.

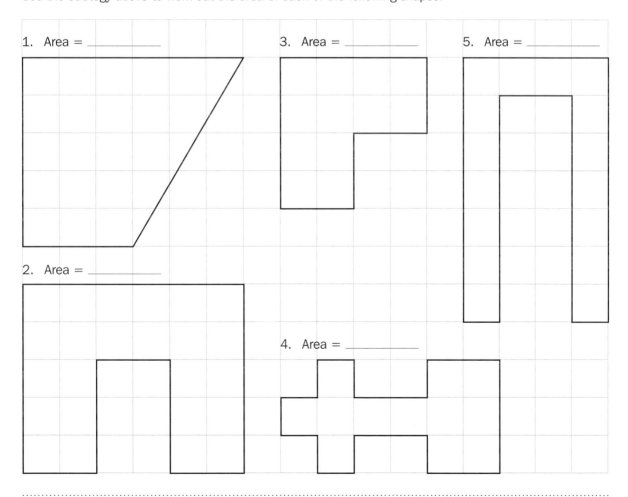

1. Area = _____

2. Area = _____

3. Area = _____

4. Area = _____

5. Area = _____

Find the area of parallelograms

To find the area of a parallelogram, multiply the base by the height.

For example:

4 cm × 7 cm = 28 cm²

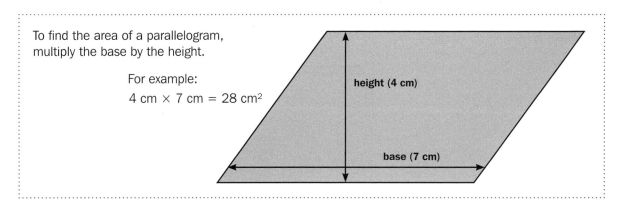

height (4 cm)

base (7 cm)

A. Find the area of each of these parallelograms.

1. Area = _____

2. Area = _____

3. Area = _____

4. Area = _____

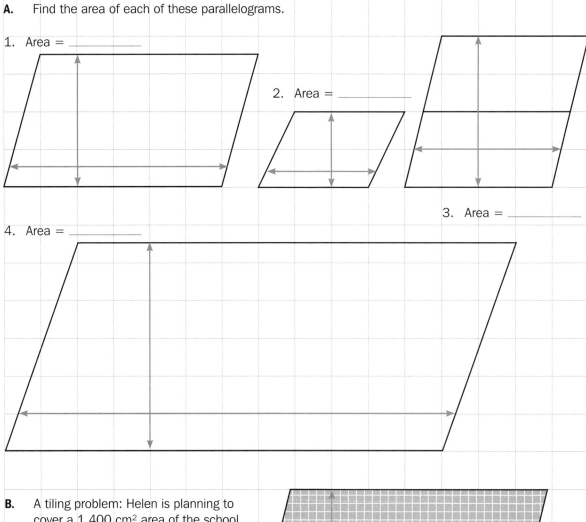

B. A tiling problem: Helen is planning to cover a 1 400 cm² area of the school garden in tiles. Calculate the number of tiles she will need to cover this area using the dimensions of the tile on the right.

Solve problems involving area

A. What's my problem? In the space below, draw a possible shape for each of these answers. Write the number of the answer next to your shape.

1. 24 m²
2. 16 m²
3. 30 m²
4. 18 m²

B. Edith is building a new cabin for her camp site. If the area needs to be between 18 m² and 22 m², what are the possible dimensions of the cabin? _____

C. A school field is 23 m by 12 m.

1. What is the area of the field? _____

2. A marquee needs to be put up on the field but it must take up no more than half of the field. The one they want to use is 180 m². Will it fit? Explain your answer.

_____

_____

D. Organisers are setting up six stages for a music festival. Find the area of each stage.

1. 12 m × 8 m   Area = _____
2. 15 m × 7.5 m   Area = _____
3. 19 m × 9 m   Area = _____
4. 25 m × 11 m   Area = _____
5. 27 m × 9.5 m   Area = _____
6. 30 m × 8.2 m   Area = _____

E. Which stage in section D above covers the largest area? _____

Task card 1   Relate-a-shape   Area

Calculate the area of each shape and use this information to explore whether any shapes are related and, if so, which ones. Jot down your findings.

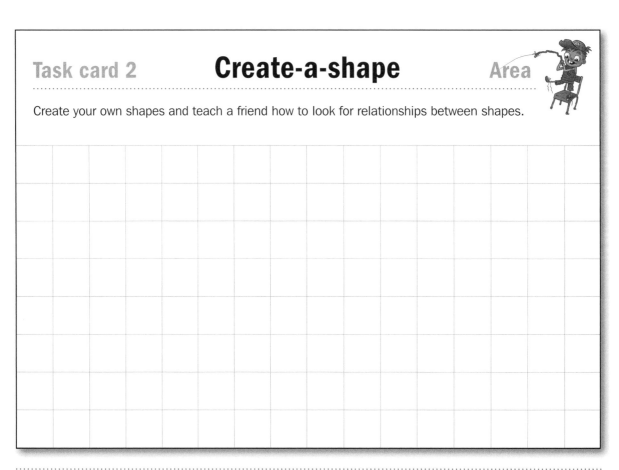

Task card 2   Create-a-shape   Area

Create your own shapes and teach a friend how to look for relationships between shapes.

Find the volume of cubes

To find the volume of a cube, multiply the lengths of each side together.

For example

1 cm

1 cm 1 cm

The volume of this cube is recorded as 1 cm³.

A. Find the volume of each of these cubes.

1. Volume = _____

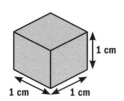

2 cm 2 cm

2 cm

3. Volume = _____

3 cm 3 cm

3 cm

5. Volume = _____

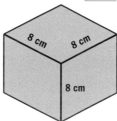

7 cm 7 cm

7 cm

7. Volume = _____

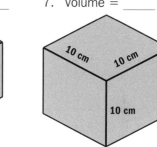

10 cm 10 cm

10 cm

2. Volume = _____

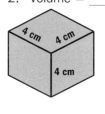

4 cm 4 cm

4 cm

4. Volume = _____

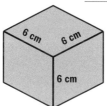

6 cm 6 cm

6 cm

6. Volume = _____

8 cm 8 cm

8 cm

B. Tom is building a tower from wooden cubes. Each cube is 1 cm³. Find the volume of each tower.

1. Volume = _____

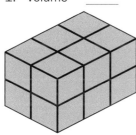

3. Volume = _____

4. Volume = _____

2. Volume = _____

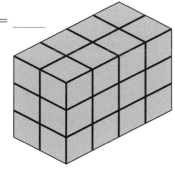

Volume

Find the volume of cuboids

To find the volume of cuboids, multiply the width by the length by the height.

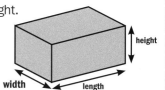

height

width | length

A. Find the volume of each of the following cuboids.

1. Volume = _____

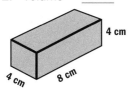

4 cm
4 cm | 8 cm

2. Volume = _____

5 cm
5 cm | 15 cm

3. Volume = _____

5 cm
5 cm | 20 cm

4. Volume = _____

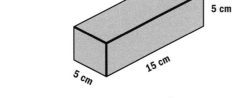

10 cm
8 cm | 20 cm

5. Volume = _____

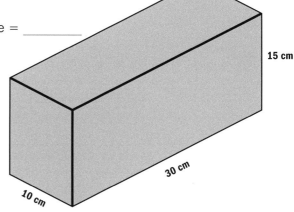

15 cm
10 cm | 30 cm

6. Volume = _____

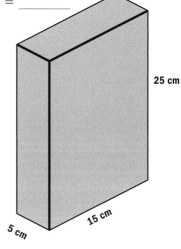

25 cm
5 cm | 15 cm

B. Shoe business: The designers of a sports shoe company are creating shoeboxes for a new range of footwear. Look at the dimensions for a single trainer on the right and suggest suitable dimensions for a box that will contain a pair of trainers.

Box dimensions = _____

10 cm high

11 cm wide | 26.26 cm long

Solve problems involving volume

A. Work out the volume of each of these boxes. Then circle the number of the box that can hold the most cornflakes.

1. 16 cm × 25 cm × 10 cm   Volume = _____

2. 15 cm × 27 cm × 10 cm   Volume = _____

3. 11 cm × 30 cm × 10 cm   Volume = _____

4. 22 cm × 29 cm × 10 cm   Volume = _____

5. 23 cm × 24 cm × 10 cm   Volume = _____

B. Use the dimensions of each swimming pool to find its volume. Then circle the number of the pool that can hold the greatest volume of water.

1. 25 m × 4 m × 2 m   Volume = _____

2. 15 m × 6 m × 2 m   Volume = _____

3. 18 m × 7 m × 2 m   Volume = _____

4. 22 m × 9 m × 2 m   Volume = _____

5. 26 m × 6 m × 2 m   Volume = _____

C. Pip needs to buy firewood. Work out the volume of each wood storage container below. Then circle the number of the container that can hold the largest amount of wood.

1. 8 m x 4 m x 6 m   Volume = _____

2. 5 m x 4 m x 7 m   Volume = _____

3. 8 m x 3 m x 4 m   Volume = _____

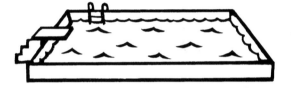

D. Jossi is building a jump for a skiing demonstration. He needs to build a jump that is approximately 5 metres long, 2 metres wide and 2.5 metres high.

1. What volume of snow will he need to make the jump? _____

2. If his truck holds approximately 6 m³, how many trips will he need to make to get all the snow he needs? _____

E. Jim is building ice towers for the Leaning Tower of Ice-a Competition. He carves blocks of ice, each of which is 12 cm long, 6 cm wide and 8 cm high. How many blocks will he need to make a tower for each of the following volumes?

Number of tower	Volume	Number of blocks needed
1	1 200 m³	
2	2 000 m³	
3	3 000 m³	

A box for locks Volume

Fluid Design is creating new packaging for a range of hair products. Your job is to create a plan for a box for the company's new hair wax, Shocking Locks. The box must be large enough to hold a container 5 cm long, 5 cm wide and 10 cm high. Your plan needs to show the dimensions of the package.

Boxed in Volume

Jed's family are moving. They hire a storage container measuring 8 metres long, 3 metres wide and 2 metres high.

Packing boxes come in 3 sizes:
- 60 cm × 60 cm × 40 cm
- 80 cm × 20 cm × 40 cm
- 80 cm × 40 cm × 40 cm.

What combination of these boxes should the family select so they make best use of the space inside the container? Record your findings and explain your method.

Read scales accurately

A. How much water is in each jug?

1. _____

3. _____
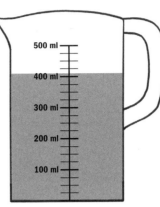

2. _____
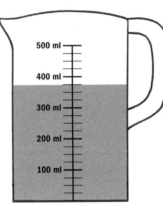

4. _____
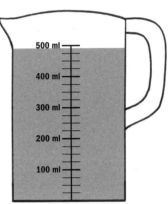

B. Approximately how much water is in each jug?

1. _____   2. _____   3. _____   4. _____

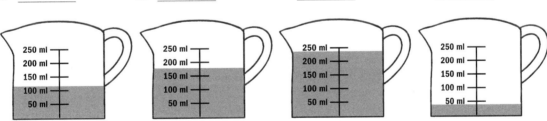

C. How much medicine (measured in millilitres) is in each syringe?

1. _____
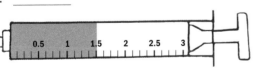

3. _____

2. _____
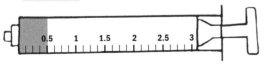

4. _____
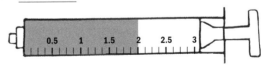

Capacity

Use scales to make sensible estimations

A. Each of these water tanks can hold 900 litres. Estimate where the following amounts of water would come up to on the tanks and draw a line on each tank to show your answer.

1. 100 litres   2. 400 litres   3. 500 litres   4. 600 litres

B. Each of these bottles can hold 1 litre. Mark each bottle to show where the amount of milk given would come up to.

1. 250 ml   2. 110 ml   3. 650 ml   4. 900 ml

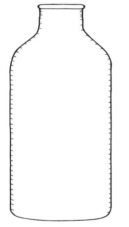

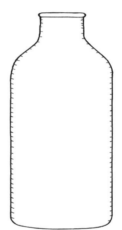
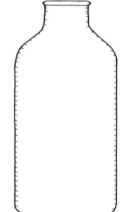

C. Each of these bottles can hold 750 ml. Draw a line on each bottle to show your estimate of where the amount of water given would come up to.

1. 250 ml   2. 125 ml   3. 375 ml   4. 700 ml

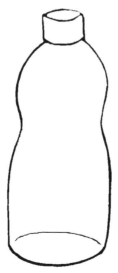
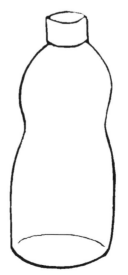
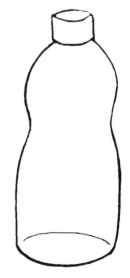

Capacity

Solve problems involving capacity

1. Paul needs 10 litres of paint to cover 54 m² of wall.

   (a) How much paint will he need to cover 66 m²? _____

   (b) How much paint will he need to cover 81 m²? _____

2. Organisers of a marathon calculate the amount of energy drinks needed for the athletes taking part. They allow 1 drink (125 ml) for each competitor for every 5 km that they run.

   (a) If 27 athletes register for the half marathon (21 km), how many litres of water are needed for them? _____

   (b) If 26 athletes register for the marathon (42 km), how many litres of energy drink are needed for them? _____

   (c) 26 athletes register for the junior race (10 km). If the organisers allow for 1 drink (125 ml) per athlete for every 3 km they run, how many litres of water are needed for the junior race?

   _____

3. If a bucket holds 12 litres of water, how many times will Jake need to refill it so that he can use the water to fill up a 150-litre water trough to the brim? _____

4. If you have 1.5 litres of fruit punch and a glass holds 125 ml, how many full glasses of fruit punch can you pour? _____

5. How many 125-ml glasses can be filled from a 5-litre container of pineapple juice? _____

6. If a water bottle holds 175 ml, how much water can 3 bottles hold? _____

7. If seven 175-ml bottles are filled with lemonade, will the amount of lemonade they hold altogether be more than 1 litre? _____

8. A bucket can hold 10 litres of water and a paddling pool can hold 124 litres.

   (a) If Hannah fills the pool with 11 bucketloads of water, will the pool be full? _____

   (b) Will 6 buckets of water fill the paddling pool to the halfway mark? _____

9. Shona collects 3.5 litres of rainwater in a barrel. How many 750 ml bottles can she fill from the barrel? _____

10. Sara needs to fill a 900-litre water tank. If she has a 12-litre bucket, how many trips will she need to make in order to fill it to the brim? _____

Game: Capacity Loopy

Use the cards on this and the following page to play a game of Capacity Loopy. Teachers can photocopy cut and laminate these cards in advance or students can prepare them independently.

Who can play?
Capacity Loopy can be played in a group or as a class.

How do you play?
1. Share out all the cards equally.

2. The player with the start card reads out the first question, "Who has …?" (Do not say the "I have …" line yet.)

3. The player who has the answer to the first question shouts out, "I have …" and gives the answer, then asks the question on their card, "Who has …?"

4. The game continues in this way, ending when the person with the start card can give their answer, "I have …".

Start card: I have 1 001 l. Who has 256 ml minus 7 ml?	**I have 249 ml.** Who has 125 ml + 19 ml?
I have 144 ml. Who has 5 l – 275 ml?	**I have 4.725 l.** Who has 3 l – 175 ml?
I have 2 825 ml. Who has 2.5 l – 300 ml?	**I have 2.2 l.** Who has 2.5 l + 600 ml?
I have 3.1 l. Who has 3 l – 750 ml?	**I have 2.25 l.** Who has 1.6 l – 900 ml?
I have 700 ml. Who has 0.6 l + 0.6 l?	**I have 1.2 l.** Who has 789 ml – 14 ml?

I have 775 ml.

Who has 188 ml + 0.5 l?

I have 688 ml.

Who has 5.6 l – 2.9 l?

I have 2.7 l.

Who has 0.5 l + 0.9 l?

I have 1.4 l.

Who has 23 ml + 10 ml?

I have 33 ml.

Who has 0.5 l – 0.28 l?

I have 0.22 l.

Who has 1.23 l + 0.8 l?

I have 2.03 ml.

Who has 5.6 l + 5.9 l?

I have 11.5 l.

Who has 5.8 l + 0.2 l?

I have 6 l.

Who has 10 l – 8.7 l?

I have 1.3 l.

Who has 2.9 l + 0.5 l?

I have 3.4 l.

Who has 7.8 + 0.9?

I have 8.7 l.

Who has 5.4 l + 2.9 l?

I have 8.3 l.

Who has 5.5 l + 0.6 l?

I have 6.1 l.

Who has 239 ml – 50 ml?

I have 189 ml.

Who has 219 ml – 20 ml?

I have 199 ml.

Who has 1 500 l – 499 l?

Lay it on the line

1. Read out each of these statements in turn and ask your partner to "lay it on the line" by either agreeing or disagreeing with the statement.

   Which of these are likely to be true?

   - A lunchbox can hold a maximum of 3 litres.
   - A cup can hold a maximum of 0.75 litres.
   - A large flask can hold a maximum of 25 ml.
   - A thimble can hold a maximum of 0.75 litres.
   - An ice cube tray can hold a maximum of 0.5 litres.
   - A teapot can hold a maximum of 1 litre.

2. Write your own statements and get your friends to "lay it on the line" for each one.

Hands free

Invent a new water carrier that can be attached to a piece of clothing suitable for a skateboarder, cyclist or snowboarder. Your water carrier must be able to hold a minimum of 1 litre. It needs to be able to be attached to a piece of clothing and it can be made from any material. You can combine existing containers (but you need to use a minimum of two) or invent your own.

Read scales accurately

We use **tonnes** (t), **kilograms** (kg), **grams** (g) and **milligrams** (mg) to measure weight.

1 t = 1 000 kg   1 000 g = 1 kg   1 g = 1 000 mg

A. Record the weight shown on each scale.

1. Weight = _____

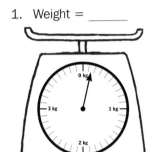

3. Weight = _____

5. Weight = _____

7. Weight = _____

2. Weight = _____

4. Weight = _____

6. Weight = _____

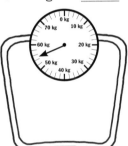

8. Weight = _____

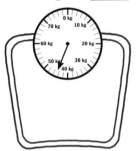

B Add another 0.25 kg of flour to each scale and write the revised weight.

1. + 0.25 kg, revised weight = _____

3. + 0.25 kg, revised weight = _____

2. + 0.25 kg, revised weight = _____

4. + 0.25 kg, revised weight = _____

Game: Weighty puzzle

You will need a copy of each of the puzzles on this and the following page. The puzzles can be enlarged onto A3 paper.

Who can play?

Work in pairs.

How do you play?

In your pair, take one puzzle each, cut it up and give it to your partner to complete. Your objective is to find equal pairs of measurements to complete the jigsaw.

Puzzle 1

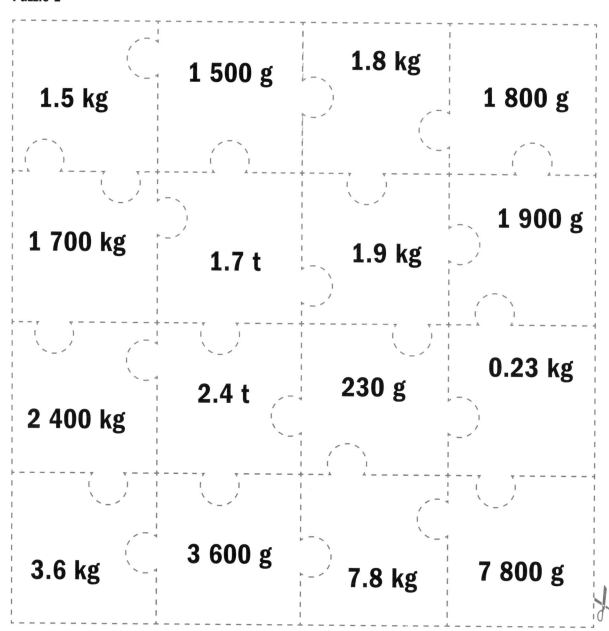

Puzzle 2

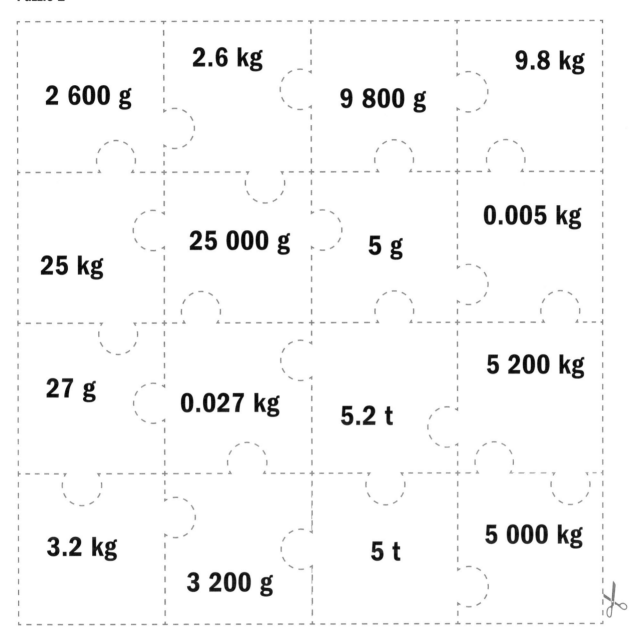

2 600 g

2.6 kg

9 800 g

9.8 kg

25 kg

25 000 g

5 g

0.005 kg

27 g

0.027 kg

5.2 t

5 200 kg

3.2 kg

3 200 g

5 t

5 000 kg

Weight

Solve problems with weight

1. Joss is clearing dirt from a forest to prepare it for a BMX course.

   (a) There are 14 tonnes of dirt and he makes 8 trips to move it all. Approximately how much dirt does he move on each trip? _____

   (b) Joss needs 0.75 tonnes of wood chippings. Wood chippings are sold in 25 kg bags. How many bags will he need? _____

   (c) Joss also needs 160 kg of concrete mix. Concrete mix is sold in 30 kg bags. How many bags will he need? _____

2. Pete is ordering supplies for his pizza restaurant. He needs 40 kilograms of high grade flour, 25 kilograms of semolina flour, 2.5 kilograms of salt and 2 kilograms of yeast.

   (a) High grade flour is sold in 2.5-kilogram bags. How many bags will he need? _____

   (b) Semolina is sold in 0.74-kilogram bags. How many bags will he need? _____

   (c) He buys six 300-g packets of salt. Will that be enough? If not, how many additional packets of salt will he need? _____

   (d) Yeast is sold in sachets. If each sachet weighs 8 grams, how many sachets will he need? _____

3. Freddy is lifting weights in the gym. He lifts a dumbbell that has four 550-gram weights. What weight does he lift in total? _____

4. Tom lifts a dumbbell that has four 900-gram weights. What weight does he lift in total? _____

5. Nathan lifts a dumbbell that has four 700-gram weights.

   (a) What weight does he lift in total? _____

   (b) How much more weight would he need to lift to make a total weight of 3.5 kilograms? _____

6. Jono carries his groceries home from the supermarket in shopping bags. Each shopping bag is strong enough to hold up to 2.5 kg. Choose a combination of his groceries that allows him to carry them home in the fewest bags possible. Write your answer on a fresh sheet of paper.

2 tins of spaghetti (415 g each)	1 block of cheese (1 kg)
2 tins of soup (415 g each)	2 packets of gingernuts (175 g each)
1 packet of cornflakes (500 g)	2 yoghurt pottles (75 g each)
1 jar of Vegemite (125 g)	1 packet of flour (1.5 kg)
3 loaves of bread (400 g each)	1 packet of hot chocolate powder (250 g)

7. The combined weight of three rugby players is 332 kg. Tom weighs 109 kg and Jed weighs less than Rich.

   (a) Which of these statements is likely to be true? Circle your choice.

      Jed weighs more than 130 kg.

      Rich weighs less than 85 kg.

      Rich weighs more than 100 kg.

   (b) What could Jed and Rich each weigh? _____

Task card 1   **A to Z**   Weight

For each letter of the alphabet, name an object that weighs less than 1 kg.

A	N
B	O
C	P
D	Q
E	R
F	S
G	T
H	U
I	V
J	W
K	X
L	Y
M	Z

- ✂ - - - - -

Task card 2   **To the rescue**   Weight

Design a life raft that can hold the body weight of one person in your class.

Time

Read analogue and digital times

A. Write the time in words under each of these analogue clocks.

1. _____

3. _____

5. _____

2. _____

4. _____

6. _____

B. Write the time in words under each of these digital clocks.

09:09

1. _____

09:14

3. _____

05:19

5. _____

13:46

2. _____

17:03

4. _____

20:28

6. _____

C. Below are different times that Jed's alarm clock shows through the day but the clock is 6 minutes slow. What is the correct time in each case? Write your answers below.

1. _____

3. _____

5. _____

2. _____

4. _____

6. _____

Time

Convert between analogue and digital time

A. Convert each analogue time to 12-hour digital time. Write your answer on the digital clock.

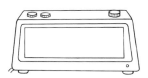

1. Quarter past 5

4. Half past twelve

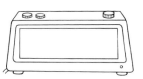

7. 18 minutes to 6

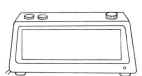

2. 21 minutes past 3

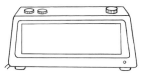

5. 6 minutes to 9

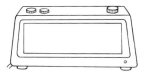

8. 10 minutes to 1

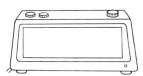

3. 13 minutes to 7

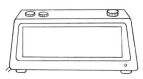

6. 21 minutes past 4

9. Quarter to 7

B. Convert each analogue and 12-hour digital time to 24-hour digital time. Write your answer on the 24-hour digital clock.

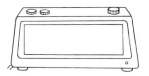

1. 5 minutes past noon

4. 1 pm

7. 13 minutes to noon

2. 6 pm

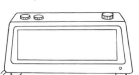

5. 8 minutes to 6 pm

8. 3:15 pm

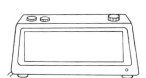

3. 20 minutes to midnight

6. 12 minutes past 7 pm

9. 8:45 pm

C. Matthew is looking up the arrival times of planes from Sydney for the day. Help him convert each 24-hour digital time to 12-hour digital time.

1. 08:00 _____

2. 13:30 _____

3. 15:45 _____

4. 20:10 _____

5. 11:35 _____

6. 19:55 _____

Time

Read and interpret timetables

A. The table shows flights departing Auckland airport to international destinations. Find the local arrival time using the information provided and write it in the final column using 12-hour digital time.

Destination	Departs	Flight time	Time difference	Local arrival time
1. Hong Kong	11:59 am	11 hours 6 minutes	−4 hours	
2. Brisbane	9:30 am	3 hours 25 minutes	−2 hours	
3. Melbourne	8:30 pm	4 hours	−2 hours	
4. Sydney	7:00 am	3 hours 30 minutes	−2 hours	
5. Cairns	7:10 pm	5 hours 15 minutes	−2 hours	

B. Solve these problems about trains. The timetable shows the daily train times from East Bay to the city centre and back again.

East Bay to City Centre										
Departs East Bay	09:05	09:25	10:15	10:45	11:15	12:00	12:55	13:30	13:55	14:30
Arrives City Centre	09:25	09:45	10:35	11:05	11:35	12:20	13:15	13:50	14:15	14:50
City Centre to East Bay										
Departs City Centre	13:00	13:15	13:45	14:15	14:30	14:45	15:00	15:15	15:30	15:45
Arrives East Bay	13:20	13:35	14:05	14:35	14:50	15:05	15:20	15:35	15:50	16:05

1. Sally is meeting a friend in the city at 11 am. What is the latest train she can catch to get there on time? _____

2. She needs to be back at East Bay by 2:30 pm but all the trains are running 9 minutes late. What is the latest train she can catch to get back in time? _____

3. Another friend takes the 13:00 train from the City Centre to East Bay. She has booked a taxi for 13:30. If the train arrives 9 minutes late, how long will she need to wait for the taxi? _____

C. Trouble with trains: The table shows the scheduled time of arrival for four different trains at the railway station. Each train is running later than scheduled. Complete the table to show the revised time at which each train will arrive.

Scheduled arrival time	Delay	Expected arrival time
1. 11:13	12 minutes	
2. 12:20	7 minutes	
3. 13:15	2 minutes	
4. 14:42	19 minutes	

Time

Solve problems involving time

A. Solve these problems about a netball competition.

On Court A Canada plays Australia at 3 pm and England plays New Zealand at 7 pm. On Court B Scotland plays Samoa at 5 pm and Fiji plays Jamaica at 8:30 pm. Each game is scheduled to run for 1 hour, excluding any extra time.

1. Ireland and Malaysia play 31 minutes after the Canada–Australia game finishes. Assuming the earlier game will not run into extra time, what time does the Ireland–Malaysia game start? _____

2. The Wales–Barbados game is due to start 45 minutes after the England–New Zealand game finishes. If it is delayed by 4 minutes, what time will the Wales–Barbados game start? _____

3. The Fiji–Jamaica game goes into 13 minutes of extra time. What time will it finish? _____

4. Maria wants to watch Scotland play Samoa then England play New Zealand. If the start of the Scotland–Samoa game is delayed by 8 minutes and the game finishes after 11 minutes of extra time, how much spare time does she have before the England–New Zealand game? _____

B. Solve these travel problems.

1. A family have booked a flight at 5:25 pm and they must check in 20 minutes before their flight leaves. To get to the airport they have to take a 45-minute train ride to the airport then a 7-minute bus ride to the terminal. If the train leaves at 4:10 pm to meet up with a connecting bus, will they get to the airport in time to check in? _____

2. Phil is catching the same flight. He leaves home at 3 pm and plans to catch the 3:15 train to the airport. The train journey is 65 minutes long. The train is running 4 minutes late and his flight is delayed by 12 minutes. How much time will he have between arriving at the airport and leaving on the plane? _____

3. Jo is catching the same flight and drives to the airport. She leaves home at 3:10 pm. The airport is 75 km from home. If she drives at an average speed of 80 km per hour, what time will she arrive at the airport? _____

C. Solve these tennis word problems.

1. A tennis match starts at noon and ends 123 minutes later. What time does it finish? _____

2. There is a 15-minute break before the second match starts. This match runs for 67 minutes. What time does it finish? _____

3. A tennis match goes for 47 minutes before rain forces the players to take an 18-minute break. The remaining part of the game takes 32 minutes. If the match started at 3 pm, what time does it finish? _____

Task card 1 On the trail

A group of friends begins the Black Forest bike trail on Monday. If the slowest person travels an average of 50 kilometres per day and the fastest person travels 55 kilometres per day, how likely is it that they will all reach the Black Barn by Saturday? Explain your answer.

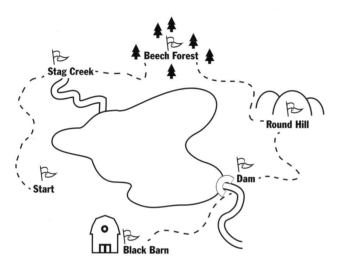

Start to Stag Creek	95 km
Stag Creek to Beech Forest	55 km
Beech Forest to Round Hill	105 km
Round Hill to the Dam	76 km
Dam to Black Barn	43 km

- - - - - - - - - - - - - - - - ✂ - - - - - - -

Task card 2 Sound bites Time

Create a recording of your favourite songs or make a podcast. The total length of time must be 2 minutes 30 seconds.

Plan the way you will use your time here.

Temperature

Read scales accurately

A. What temperature does each thermometer show?

1.  _____

2. 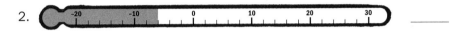 _____

3.  _____

4.  _____

B. What temperature does each dial show?

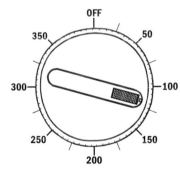

1. _____

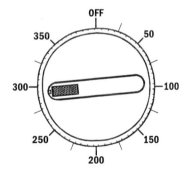

2. _____

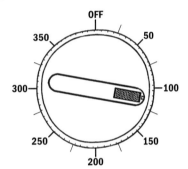

3. _____

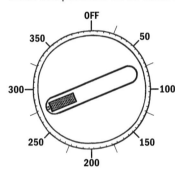

4. _____

C. Show each temperature below on a thermometer.

1. 22° Celsius

2. −11° Celsius

3. −8° Celsius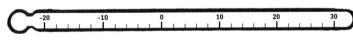

4. 19° Celsius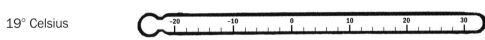

Temperature

Solve problems involving temperature

A. The table shows the temperatures recorded at Rocky Hill during one week of a ski season. Use the information below to complete it.

Daily temperature on Rocky Hill

Day	Sunday	Monday	Tuesday	Wednesday	Thursday	Friday	Saturday
Temperature	–6°C		–2°C			–7°C	

Monday's temperature was 2 degrees warmer than Sunday's.

Wednesday's temperature was 3 degrees cooler than Tuesday's.

Thursday's temperature was 4 degrees warmer than Monday's.

Saturday's temperature was halfway between Tuesday's and Thursday's.

B. Use the information in the table to answer the questions below.

Current world temperatures		
Adelaide 7°C	Bangkok 25°C	Sydney 6°C
Beijing 20°C	Brisbane 7°C	Wellington 8°C
Cairns 17°C	Canberra 0°C	Johannesburg 1°C
Dubai 10°C	Hong Kong 29°C	Toronto 14°C
London 13°C	Melbourne 7°C	Auckland 9°C
New York 23°C	Edinburgh 8°C	Hobart 5°C

1. Find the city with the coolest temperature. _____

2. Find the city with the third coolest temperature. _____

3. Find the second warmest city. _____

4. If you are looking for a warm place you could go for a holiday in the season when the temperatures above were recorded, find a place in the northern hemisphere you could visit.

   _____

5. Which is the warmest city in Australia? _____

6. What is the difference in temperature between London and Edinburgh? _____

7. A family in New York are planning to go on holiday to a location that is in winter. Recommend a city and explain why you are recommending it. _____

C. The Big Chill: Work out how much the temperature changes on each ski run. Assume it changes at a steady rate from the top to the bottom.

1. At the top of the Mogul chairlift, it is –5° Celsius. At the bottom of the lift, it is 3° Celsius. What is the temperature halfway up? _____

2. At the top of the Duet Delight chairlift, it is –8° Celsius. At the bottom of the lift, it is 2° Celsius. What is the temperature halfway up? _____

This activity tests the effectiveness of insulation materials.

In pairs, invent an insulation layer to keep a cup of hot chocolate warm. It can be made from any material.

You will need boiling water, milk, hot chocolate, plastic cups and a lid, a thermometer and a stopwatch. The challenge is to keep your hot chocolate from cooling down.

Record the temperature of your hot chocolate at the start. Check your hot chocolate every 2 minutes and record the temperature. The temperature in your classroom may also affect your results so adapt the frequency with which you check your hot chocolate as needed.

Graph your findings in the space below. Which insulation layer was the most successful? Why did it succeed?

Task card 2 **Make a baked Alaska** Temperature

Baked Alaska is a pudding made from sponge and ice cream which is smothered in meringue then baked in the oven until the meringue is cooked but the ice cream remains solid. The meringue acts as an insulator and stops the ice cream from melting.

Your challenge is to create the best basked Alaska, which keeps the ice cream inside it solid.

Share your findings with the class.

How to make 4–6 baked Alaska puddings

One sponge cake
650 ml ice cream
4 egg whites
225 g caster sugar

1. Preheat the oven to 230° Celsius.

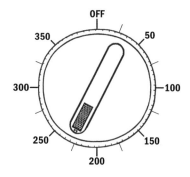

2. Prepare the meringue mix by beating 4 egg whites until they form soft peaks and gradually add in sugar until the mixture is glossy.

3. Cut out a circle of sponge and lay it on a piece of baking paper.

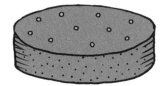

4. Place 1 large scoop of ice cream on the sponge, leaving a border for the meringue mix.

5. Cover the ice cream and sponge with a thick layer of meringue. Make sure that there are no gaps!

6. Bake in a hot oven until the meringue is golden (approximately 3–4 minutes).

Read scales accurately

A. Record the speed shown on each speedometer.

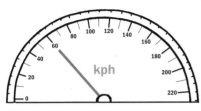

1. _____

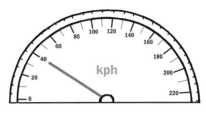

3. _____

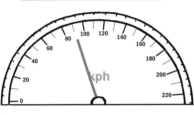

2. _____

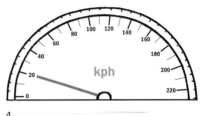

4. _____

B. Write the approximate speed on each speedometer.

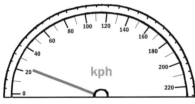

1. _____

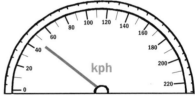

3. _____

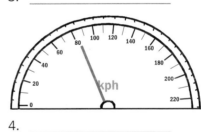

2. _____

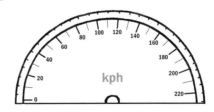

4. _____

C. Draw the dial on each speedometer to show the speed recorded.

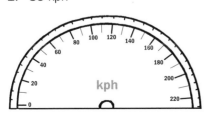

1. 85 kph

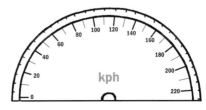

3. 46 kph

2. 15 kph

4. 105 kph

Speed

Solve problems involving speed

> For the problems below, use the prompts to remind you:
>
> **Speed = Distance ÷ Time**
> **Distance = Speed × Time**
> **Time = Distance ÷ Speed**

1. Debbie walks for 3 hours. If she walks at an average of 2.5 km per hour, how far will she walk in 3 hours? _____

2. Tom walks 3.5 km per hour. How far will he walk in 4 hours? _____

3. Mike walks 3.5 km per hour. If he walks 10 km, how long will it take him? _____

4. Meg runs 10 km in 72 minutes. What is her average speed per kilometre? _____

5. Jon runs 10 km in 55 minutes. What is his average speed per kilometre? _____

6. If Tom runs an average of 1 kilometre every 4 minutes 30 seconds, how long will it take him to run 10 km? _____

7. Jess runs 10 km in 57 minutes at a consistent speed.

    (a) What is her average speed per kilometre? _____

    (b) How long will it take her to run the following distances? 8 km _____ 13 km _____

8. Runner 1 completes 7 km in 28 minutes; Runner 2 completes 12 km in 54 minutes; and Runner 3 completes 15 km in 52 minutes and 30 seconds. Which runner has the fastest speed per kilometre? _____

9. The distance from the beach to the city is 160 km.

    (a) If Dad gets there in 1 hour 20 minutes, what speed has he travelled at, assuming he has driven at a constant speed? _____

    (a) If he travels at a constant speed of 96 kph, how long will it take him to get to the city? _____

10. A racing driver is test-driving a new car on a racing circuit.

    (a) If she is driving at 150 kilometres per hour, how many complete 250-metre laps can she do in 10 minutes? _____

    (b) How many complete 250-metre laps can she do in 20 minutes if she travels at 180 kilometres per hour? _____

Task card 1 — Cycling tour

Each cyclist on a tour must cover a stage each day. Use the following information to answer the true or false questions on the right.

Stage	Distance
Stage 1	120 km
Stage 2	65 km
Stage 3	150.5 km
Stage 4	175.5 km
Stage 5	225 km

On average, Tom cycles at 20 kilometres per hour, Jed cycles at 18 kilometres per hour, and Ryan cycles at 25 kilometres per hour.

Circle True or False for each of these statements.

1. Both Tom and Jed finish stage 1 in less than 5 hours.
   True   False

2. Ryan finishes stage 5 in less than 10 hours.
   True   False

3. Tom and Ryan take more than 5 hours to finish stage 3.
   True   False

4. Ryan takes more than 27 hours to complete all five stages.
   True   False

5. If the winner of the tour takes 28 hours to complete the distance, his average speed per hour would be more than 25 kilometres per hour.
   True   False

Task card 2 — The world's fastest ...

Find a world speed record that interests you. Do you think it is possible to break this record in your lifetime? Are there some speed records that seem unlikely to be improved on? Give reasons for your answer.

Recognise 90° angles

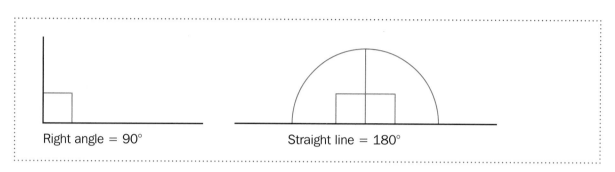

Right angle = 90°   Straight line = 180°

A. Circle any marked angle that shows 90°.

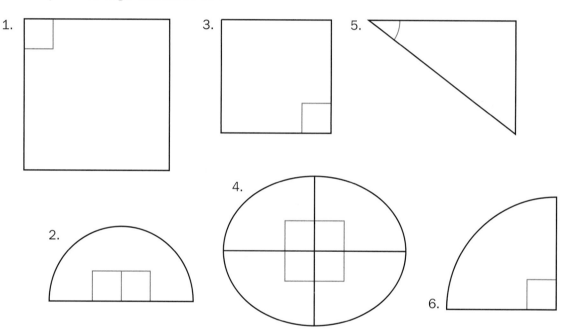

B. Show the 90° angle or angles on each of these shapes.

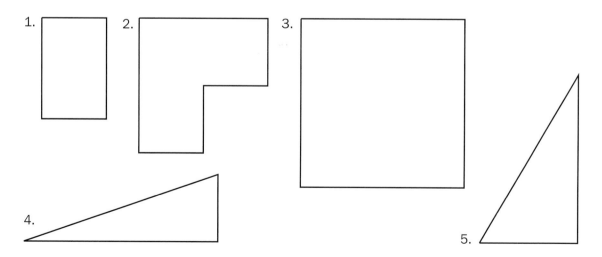

Angles

Recognise acute, obtuse and reflex angles

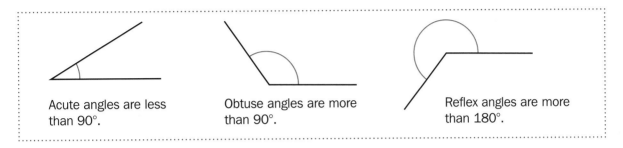

Acute angles are less than 90°.

Obtuse angles are more than 90°.

Reflex angles are more than 180°.

Mark the acute angle or angles on each shape that has them.

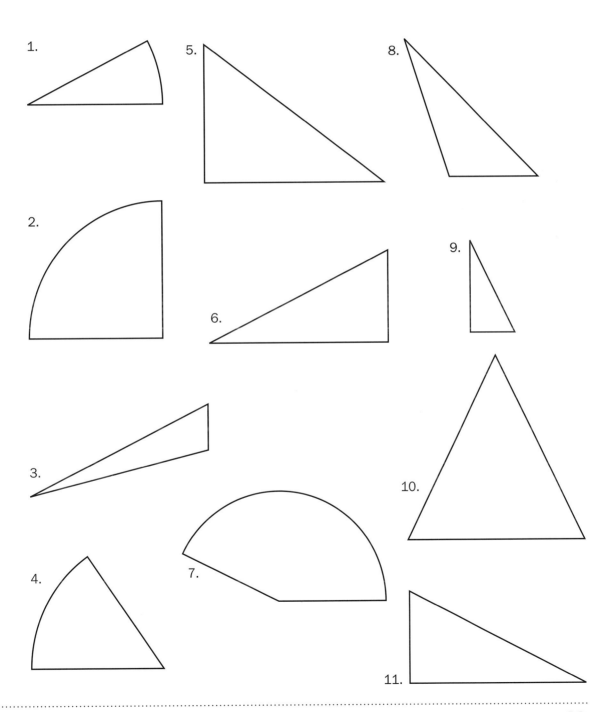

1.

2.

3.

4.

5.

6.

7.

8.

9.

10.

11.

Measure angles

A. Use a protractor to measure these angles and write your answer under the angle.

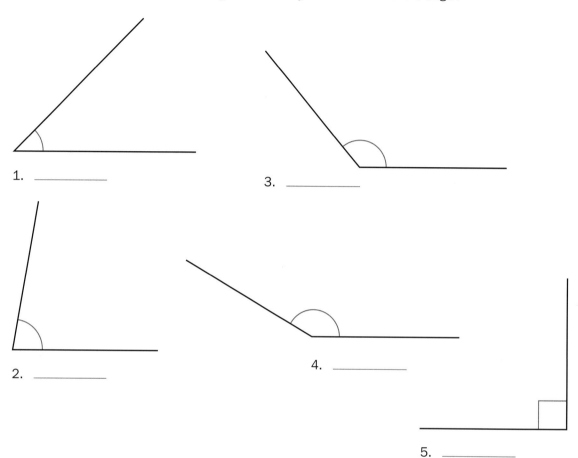

1. _____

3. _____

2. _____

4. _____

5. _____

B. A straight line is 180°. Find the value of each missing angle without using a protractor.

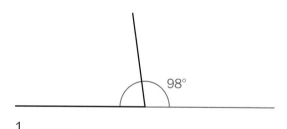

1. _____

3. _____

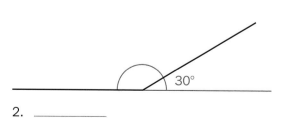

2. _____

4. _____

Use angles for bearings

We use bearings to help us explain direction.
When we use bearings, we always take the direction from north.

For example: Andy is on a bush walk. He uses a compass to guide him.

If he travels in the direction of the arrow,
he is walking on a bearing of 90°.

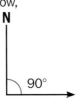

90°

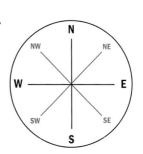

Use your knowledge of angles to help you find the following bearings.

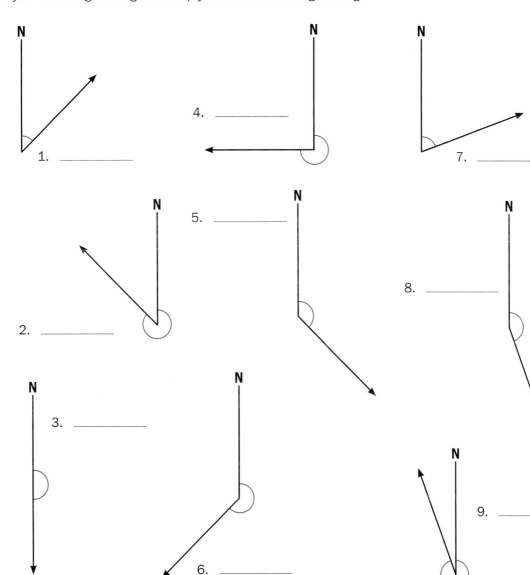

1. _____

2. _____

3. _____

4. _____

5. _____

6. _____

7. _____

8. _____

9. _____

Page 6

A.

1. 10 cm
2. 6 cm
3. 3.5 cm
4. 11.8 cm
5. 3.2 cm

B.

1. 60 cm
2. 40 cm
3. 70 cm
4. 15 mm
5. 48 mm

Page 7

1. 3 cm
2. 3.5 cm
3. 5 cm
4. 4 cm
5. 6 cm
6. 9 cm
7. 5 cm
8. 6 cm
9. 2 cm
10. 5 cm
11. 2 cm
12. 5 cm

Page 8

1. 65 mm
2. 59 mm
3. 13 mm
4. 75 mm
5. 88 mm
6. 45 mm
7. 27 mm
8. 8 mm
9. 90 mm
10. 33 mm

Page 9

A.

1. 3.5 cm
2. 6.5 cm
3. 5 cm
4. 7 cm
5. 2.5 cm

B.

1. 22 mm
2. 31 mm
3. 41 mm
4. 37 mm
5. 19 mm

C.
1.2 cm = 12 mm;
15 mm = 1.5 cm;
34 cm = 340 mm;
9.9 cm = 99 mm;
8.9 cm = 89 mm;
27 mm = 2.7 cm;
109 cm = 1 090 mm

Page 10

A.

1. 1 500
2. 1 750
3. 0.22
4. 2 750
5. 2 800
6. 0.195
7. 1.236
8. 5.879

B.

Jan 1 705 m, 1.705 km
Henry 1 860 m, 1.86 km
Miriama 1 942 m, 1.942 km
Kes 1 964 m, 1.964 km
Jenny 1 699 m, 1.699 km

C.

1. 101.106 km
2. 97.204 km
3. 126.125 km
4. 74.102 km
5. 9.879 km
6. 105.586 km
7. 54.125 km
8. 77.012 km

D.

1. 2 400 m
2. 5 800 m
3. 1 700 m
4. 4 500 m

Page 11

1. 24 cm
2. 20 cm
3. 8 cm
4. 17.5 cm
5. 22 cm
6. 24 cm
7. 32 cm
8. 12 cm

Page 12

A.

1. 28 cm
2. 24 cm
3. 20 cm
4. 30 cm

B.

1. $x = 3$ cm,
   perimeter = 20 cm
2. $x = 3$ cm, $y = 4$ cm,
   perimeter = 22 cm
3. $x = 3$ cm, $y = 3.5$ cm,
   perimeter =18 cm

C.

1. $x = 5$ m
2. $a = 12$ m

Page 13

A. *Teacher checks answers.*

B.

1. 200 m
2. 625 m
3. 475 m
4. 675 m
5. 1 000 m

C.

1. 84 m
2. 86 m
3. 76 m
4. 59 m

D.

1. 260 lengths
2. 148 lengths
3. 380 lengths

E.

1. (b)
2. (c)

Page 15

A.

1. 35 cm²
2. 12 cm²
3. 18 cm²
4. 24.5 cm²

B.

1. 120 m²
2. 855 m²
3. 1 440 m²
4. 6 030 m²
5. 4 290 m²
6. 325 m²
7. 2 880 m²
8. 180 m²
9. 760 m²
10. 672 m²

Page 16

1. 14 cm²
2. 9 cm²
3. 35 cm²
4. 4.5 cm²
5. 18 cm²
6. 28 cm²
7. 20 cm²

Answers

Page 17

1. 22.5 cm²
2. 24 cm²
3. 12 cm²
4. 12 cm²
5. 16 cm²

Page 18

A.
1. 21 cm²
2. 6 cm²
3. 16 cm²
4. 66 cm²

B. Tile = 28 cm²;
50 tiles needed

Page 19

A. *Shapes could be:*
1. 6 m × 4 m
2. 4 m × 4 m
3. 6 m × 5 m
4. 6 m × 3 m

B. 4 m × 5 m

C.
1. 276 m²
2. No, it is too big. The area of the marquee needs to be 138 m² or smaller to fit.

D.
1. 96 m²
2. 112.5 m²
3. 171 m²
4. 275 m²
5. 256.5 m²
6. 246 m²

E. Stage 4

Page 21

A.
1. 8 cm³
2. 64 cm³
3. 27 cm³
4. 216 cm³
5. 343 cm³
6. 512 cm³
7. 1 000 cm³

B.
1. 12 cm³
2. 24 cm³
3. 18 cm³
4. 49 cm³

Page 22

A.
1. 128 cm³
2. 375 cm³
3. 500 cm³
4. 1 600 cm³
5. 4 500 cm³
6. 1 875 cm³

B. *Answers will vary but could include*: 30.26 cm x 15 cm x 14 cm

Page 23

A.
1. 4 000 cm³
2. 4 050 cm³
3. 3 300 cm³
4. 6 380 cm³ (can hold the most cornflakes)
5. 5 520 cm³

B.
1. 200 m³
2. 180 m³
3. 252 m³
4. 396 m³ (can hold the greatest volume of water)
5. 312 m³

C.
1. 192 m³ (can hold the largest amount of wood)
2. 140 m³
3. 96 m³

D.
1. 25 m³
2. 5 trips

E.
1. 209
2. 348
3. 521

Page 25

A.
1. 125 ml
2. 375 ml
3. 410 ml
4. 490 ml

B.
1. 110 ml
2. 180 ml
3. 240 ml
4. 45 ml

C.
1. 1.5 ml
2. 0.5 ml
3. 2 ml
4. 1.75 ml

Page 26

Teacher checks all answers.

Page 27

1. (a) 13 litres (b) 15 litres
2. (a) 16.875 litres
   (b) 29.25 litres (c) 13 litres
3. 13
4. 12
5. 40
6. 525 ml
7. Yes, 7 bottles hold 1 225 ml.
8. (a) No, 11 buckets hold 110 litres. (b) No.
9. 4 full bottles.
10. 75

Page 31

A.
1. 150 g
2. 725 g
3. 1.5 kg
4. 2.75 kg
5. 76 kg
6. 55 kg
7. 64 kg
8. 45 kg

B.
1. 3.75 kg
2. 2 kg
3. 1.75 kg
4. 135 g

Answers

Page 34

1. (a) 1.75 tonnes
   (b) 30 bags (c) 6 bags
2. (a) 16 bags (b) 34 bags
   (c) No, he needs 3 extra packets. (d) 250 sachets
3. 2.2 kg
4. 3.6 kg
5. (a) 2.8 kg (b) 0.7 kg
6. *Many combinations are possible. Teacher checks answers.*
7. (a) Rich weighs more than 100 kg.
   (b) Jed 110 kg, Rich 113 kg

Page 36

A.
1. 19 minutes past 12
2. 12 minutes to 5
3. 26 minutes past 4
4. 18 minutes to 8
5. 9 minutes to 3
6. 18 minutes past 7

B.
1. nine "o" nine
2. thirteen forty-six
3. nine fourteen
4. seventeen "o" three
5. five nineteen
6. twenty twenty-eight

C.
1. 7 minutes to 1
2. 23 minutes past 4
3. 28 minutes past 7
4. 18 minutes to 3
5. 22 minutes past 11
6. 5 minutes to 6

Page 37

A.
1. 5:15
2. 3:21
3. 6:47
4. 12:30
5. 8:54
6. 4:21
7. 5:42
8. 12:50
9. 6:45

B.
1. 12:05
2. 18:00
3. 23:40
4. 13:00
5. 17:52
6. 19:12
7. 11:47
8. 15:15
9. 20:45

C.
1. 8:00 am
2. 1:30 pm
3. 3:45 pm
4. 8:10 pm
5. 11:35 am
6. 7:55 pm

Page 38

A.
1. 6:05 pm
2. 10:55 am
3. 10:30 pm
4. 8:30 am
5. 10:25 pm

B.
1. 10:15
2. 13:45
3. 1 minute

C.
1. 11:25
2. 12:27
3. 13:17
4. 15:01

Page 39

A.
1. 4:31 pm
2. 8:49 pm
3. 9:43 pm
4. 41 minutes

B.
1. Yes, they will have 3 minutes to spare.
2. 1 hour and 13 minutes
3. 4:06 pm

C.
1. 2:03 pm   3.   4:37 pm
2. 3:25 pm

Page 40

Task card 1
It is unlikely as the slowest rider would still be at Round Hill on Saturday.

Page 41

A.
1. 16° Celsius
2. −6° Celsius
3. −8° Celsius
4. 26° Celsius

B.
1. 275° Celsius
2. 120° Celsius
3. 110° Celsius
4. 290° Celsius

C. *Teacher checks answers.*

54 © TTS Group Ltd, 2012

Answers

Page 42

A. Monday – 4°C; Wednesday –5°C; Thursday 0°C; Saturday –1°C

B.
1. Canberra
2. Hobart
3. Bangkok
4. *Various answers are possible.*
5. Cairns
6. 5° Celsius
7. *Various answers are possible.*

C.
1. –1°C   2. –3°C

Page 45

A.
1. 60 kph   3. 40 kph
2. 90 kph   4. 20 kph

B.
1. 23 kph   3. 48 kph
2. 99 kph   4. 81 kph

C. *Teacher checks answers.*

Page 46

1. 7.5 km
2. 14 km
3. 2 hours, 51 minutes, 25 seconds
4. 7.2 kph
5. 5.5 kph
6. 45 minutes
7. (a) 5.7 kph
   (b) 45 minutes; 1 hour 14 minutes
8. Runner 3
9. (a) 120 kph
   (b) 1 hour 40 minutes
10. (a) 100 (b) 240

Page 47

Task card 1
1. False   4. True
2. True   5. True
3. True

Pages 48–49

Teacher checks answers.

Page 50

A.
1. 45°   4. 150°
2. 80°   5. 90°
3. 130°

B.
1. 82°   3. 60°
2. 150°   4. 20°

Page 51

1. 45°   6. 225°
2. 315°   7. 70°
3. 180°   8. 160°
4. 270°   9. 340°
5. 135°